Better Homes and Gardens®

Garden Diary

MEREDITH® BOOKS

DES MOINES

MEREDITH® BOOKS
PRESIDENT: JOSEPH J. WARD
VICE PRESIDENT AND EDITORIAL DIRECTOR: ELIZABETH P. RICE

Better Homes and Gardens® Garden Diary
EDITOR: DEBRA D. FELTON
ART DIRECTOR: TRACY S. DEVENNEY
SENIOR EDITOR: MARSHA JAHNS

PHOTOGRAPHERS: ALAN ABRAMOWITZ; ERNEST BRAUN;
KIM BRUN STUDIOS, INC.; LAURIE DICKSON; TIM FIELDS; D. RANDOLPH FOULDS;
SUSAN GILMORE; ED GOHLICH; JAY GRAHAM; KARLIS GRANTS; BILL HELMS;
WILLIAM N. HOPKINS, HOPKINS ASSOCIATES; TERRY HUSEBYE; ROY INMAN; JON JENSEN;
MIKE JENSEN; PETER KRUMHARDT; MARIS/SEMEL; BARBARA MARTIN; CHRIS OSTLIND;
MARY CAROLYN PINDAR; ERIC ROTH; LINDA JOAN SMITH; WILLIAM STITES;
PERRY STRUSE; JUDITH WATTS

According to a Spanish proverb, "More things grow in the garden than the gardener sows." For those who live a gardener's life, each day of the year does in fact bring much more: greater surprises, deeper introspection, and a constant renewal of hope. To remind you of those abundant lessons from the garden, this book is filled with quotes, ideas, and inspirations. Whether you use it to plan your garden or other parts of your life, we hope it will serve as your own measure of growth, guiding you throughout the seasons.

JANUARY

New Year's Resolutions

As you dream of spring, keep these earth-wise gardening tips in mind.

🍃 Conserve water by grouping plants with similar moisture needs, then watering during the cool, calm hours of early morning.

🍃 Reduce the size of your lawn and devote more yard space to ground covers, which have low moisture requirements.

🍃 Rely on natives and wildflowers. Plants that are indigenous to your region are accustomed to your climate and soil type, and they're immune to pests and diseases.

🍃 Say no to bugs with nontoxic controls. Predatory insects, such as ladybugs, praying mantises, and lacewings, keep bad bugs at bay.

1 _____

2 _____

3 _____

4 _____

5 _____

6 _____

7 _____

8 _____

9 _____

10 _____

11 _____

12 _____

13 _____

14 _____

15 _____

No cloud above, no earth below—
A universe of sky and snow.
—*John Greenleaf Whittier*

16 _____

17 _____

18 _____

19 _____

20 _____

21 _____

22 _____

23 _____

24 _____

25 _____

26 _____

27 _____

28 _____

29 _____

30 _____

31 _____

Ring out the old, ring in the new,
Ring, happy bells, across the snow;
The year is going, let him go;
Ring out the false, ring in the true.
—*Alfred Tennyson*

ATTRACTING WILDLIFE

To Attract Butterflies...

Plant chives, coneflower, cornflower, cosmos, dahlia, flossflower, globe amaranth, impatiens, lantana, lavender, lilac, pussy willow, sedum, strawflower, and tithonia.

Care and Feeding

Water. Keep birdbaths shallow, clean, and filled, even during the winter. If you can provide a pond, include some shallow, calm water and use logs or flat stones to create partially submerged perches. Turtles and frogs will thrive in the water itself, and larger animals, such as rabbits, raccoons, opossums, and deer, will visit larger ponds.

Food. Trees top the list of food sources, bearing leaves, fruits, and berries, and luring insects that are a treat for birds. Shrubs, especially savory fruit-bearing ones, attract wildlife. Creatures will be attracted to almost any flowers, but bright-colored, potently fragrant, nectar-rich flowers draw animals by the droves.

Protection. Creatures need escapes from fierce weather. You can create a great habitat for small mammals, such as chipmunks, rabbits, raccoons, skunks, or opossums, by piling up brush or boulders, perhaps burying PVC pipe at the bottom. Leave a dead tree alone, unless it's posing a risk; it will create a great home for birds and animals, plus provide an insect banquet for birds.

FOR THE BIRDS

If you choose to feed birds, make sure you continue feeding them during the cold months. They will rely on you. Even if you have a bird feeder, many birds, such as sparrows and juncos, prefer to feed on the ground. Scatter food on the ground for them, and free up your feeder for more colorful species.

To keep squirrels from raiding birds' dinner, hang feeders where squirrels can't drop down on them, or use a pole with a skirt so the squirrel can't shimmy up. Some squirrelproof feeders close the food tray because of the weight of the squirrel, but beware—a hungry squirrel may gnaw through a feeder.

Bird Cakes

It's easy to invite feathered friends into your garden when you mix up a batch of these homemade treats. They'll attract a wide variety of birds.

1 part peanut butter
1 part birdseed
5 parts cornmeal
1 part melted beef suet
Spoon the mixture into paper-lined muffin tins and cool until hardened.

I hope you love birds, too. It is economical.

It saves going to Heaven.

—Emily Dickinson

7

FEBRUARY

Tips from a Master Gardener

Winter is a good time to collect ideas from other gardeners. Here are a few from Jerry Baker, America's Master Gardener.

 Each spring before spading, apply to the garden a mixture of 1 pound of sugar for each 50 pounds of any brand of garden food. "Plants manufacture sugars and starches," Jerry says. "Give them a form they can take immediately if they're little babies."

 For spring and fall fertilizing, add one 4-pound box of epsom salt to any brand of 2,500-square-foot formula lawn fertilizer. The magnesium releases nitrogen within the ground, making grass greener and stronger.

 Wear golf shoes when working in the yard. The spikes punch holes through the matted ground surface, allowing water to seep in.

1

2

3

4

5

6

7

8

9

10

11

12

13

14

15

You cannot plough a field by turning it over in your mind.

—*Anonymous*

16 _____

17 _____

18 _____

If February give much snow
A fine Summer it doth foreshow.

—*English rhyme*

19 _____

20 _____

21 _____

22 _____

23 _____

24 _____

25 _____

26 _____

27 _____

28 _____

29 _____

Plans for the Season

_____

_____

_____

_____

_____

_____

SPRING

*Buttercups and daisies—
Oh, the pretty flowers!
Coming ere the Springtime,
To tell of sunny hours.
When the trees are leafless;
When the fields are bare;
Buttercups and daisies
Spring up here and there.*

—Mary Howitt

11

Designing a Cottage Garden

❧ Avoid the temptation to plant your garden in neat, straight rows. Instead, arrange flowers in irregular-size clumps, each flowing into the next in unbroken waves of color.

❧ Choose an array of hues—not just two or three dominant colors—to enhance the garden's informal diversity.

❧ If you're planting annuals from seed, choose seed blends that mix several colors in one packet.

❧ Bend the rules about planting flowers in order of uniform heights. Think, instead, in terms of height ranges. Shorter species (less than 18 inches tall) should be placed near the front of the border. Blooms that reach more than 2 feet in height belong in the back.

1

2

3

4

5

6

7

8

9

10

11

12

13

14

15

A little wind kindles, much puts out the fire.

—George Herbert

16 _____

17 _____

18 _____

19 _____

20 _____

21 _____

22 _____

23 _____

24 _____

25 _____

26 _____

27 _____

28 _____

29 _____

30 _____

31 _____

A light exists in Spring

Not present in the year

at any other period

When March is scarcely here.

—Emily Dickinson

13

In all places, then, and in all seasons,
Flowers expand their light and soul-like wings,
Teaching us by most persuasive reasons
How akin they are to human things.

—Henry Wadsworth Longfellow

APRIL

Water Gardens

✒ Locate a garden pond in an area that receives about five hours of sunlight a day. Plants may suffer with any less, and fish may become uncomfortably hot with any more.

✒ Larger ponds are actually easier to maintain and are less likely to overheat. Too much heat can stress fish and lead to algae buildup.

✒ If you stock your pond with fish (koi is a popular choice), figure on 10 gallons of water per inch of fish to avoid overcrowding, which can lead to disease.

✒ Water lilies, the easiest water plant to grow, bloom from late spring to early fall. Perennial tubers, they can be stored indoors through the winter and replanted in spring.

1

2

3

4

5

6

7

8

9

10

11

12

13

14

15

Rainbow to windward, foul fall the day;
Rainbow to leeward, damp runs away.

—*Sailors' Rhyme*

16 _____

17 _____

18 _____

19 _____

20 _____

21 _____

22 _____

23 _____

24 _____

25 _____

26 _____

27 _____

28 _____

29 _____

30 _____

April, April,
Laugh thy girlish laughter;
Then, the moment after,
Weep thy girlish tears.

—*Sir William Watson*

HERB GARDENING

Harvesting Herbs

Depending on the variety, herbs may be ready to harvest from June until frost. Snip your favorite specimens regularly for drying indoors. If you're harvesting flowers, pick them when the blossoms are fully open. Leaves, however, should be harvested before the plants bloom. Strip the leaves from the bottom 6 inches of each stem, then gather several stems into a bundle, securing them with a rubber band. Hang the bunches upside down to dry.

GARLIC HERB VINEGAR

3 large cloves garlic, peeled

1 cup (approximately) fresh herb sprigs, such as basil, oregano, thyme, or lovage, rinsed and patted dry

3 cups white wine or cider vinegar

Place garlic cloves in bottom of a decorative 1-quart (or two 12-ounce) glass bottle(s). Loosely pack in a small bundle of herbs. In a large saucepan, heat vinegar until hot, but not boiling. Pour through a funnel over garlic and herbs. Seal with a cork. Allow to stand in a dark, cool place for at least 2 weeks. Makes 3 cups.

*F*or comfort when you have a cold, make tea from rose hips, a good source of vitamin C. Other medicinal herbs include sage, chamomile, bee balm, thyme, comfrey, and calendula.

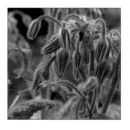

Favorite Culinary Herbs

Oregano. Strong, spicy flavor. Add to sauces and pasta salads.

Tarragon. Spicy, sharp flavor with licoricelike overtones. Try it in marinades for grilled meats.

Sweet basil. Robust, peppery flavor. Pairs perfectly with tomatoes and tossed salads.

Dill. Delicate and refreshing taste. Excellent with fish and seafood or vegetables.

*P*lace fragrant herbs, such as lavender, close to paths so you can enjoy their sweet aromas as you brush past them. Or plant creeping varieties, such as thyme, between stepping stones.

M A Y

Perennials

🌿 Garden centers and nurseries sell perennials in containers of varying sizes. To ensure flowers the first season, purchase bigger plants.

🌿 Plant perennials at the same depth they grew in the pots, spacing them to allow for their mature sizes.

🌿 Water them daily for the first week, then every few days after that.

🌿 Perennials bloom more vigorously if they're divided every few years. Most species should be divided in early spring, as soon as new growth appears.

🌿 A few perennials, including peony, iris, and poppy, should be divided in late summer or early fall.

1 _____

2 _____

3 _____

4 _____

5 _____

6 _____

7 _____

8 _____

9 _____

10 _____

11 _____

12 _____

13 _____

14 _____

15 _____

He who plants a garden, plants happiness.

—Chinese proverb

16 _____

17 _____

18 _____

19 _____

20 _____

21 _____

22 _____

23 _____

24 _____

25 _____

26 _____

27 _____

28 _____

29 _____

30 _____

31 _____

All nature's imps triumph

whiles joyful May dost last;

When May is gone, of all the year

the pleasant time is past.

—Richard Edwards

Plans for the Season

_____

_____

_____

_____

_____

_____

_____

_____

SUMMER

*I never had any other
desire so strong and so like
to covetousness, as that
one which I have had
always, that I might be
master at last of a small
house and large garden.*

—Abraham Cowley

JUNE

Quicker Composting

Jim Bennett, host of television's "Backyard America," believes this home-mixed additive cuts the decomposition time of compost by one-third.

🌿 Fill a 5-gallon bucket with 4 gallons of water and add:

1 can stale, nonpasteurized beer (the bacteria help break down compost)

1/2 cup high-nitrogen fertilizer, such as 20-20-20

1 shovelful of old compost or 2 shovels of new soil

🌿 Let mixture sit overnight. When building a pile, layer dirt and compost (grass clippings, straw, leaves) like the layers of a cake, pouring one quart of this solution on each layer.

1	
2	
3	
4	
5	
6	
7	
8	
9	
10	
11	
12	
13	
14	
15	

Colors are the smiles of nature.

—*Leigh Hunt*

16

17

18

19

20

21

22

23

24

25

26

27

28

29

30

It is the month of June,
The month of leaves and roses,
When pleasant sights salute the eyes,
And pleasant scents the noses.

—*N.P. Willis*

*A*nd because the breath of flowers is far sweeter in the
air (where it comes and goes, like the warbling of
music) than in the hand, therefore nothing is more fit
for that delight than to know what be the flowers and
plants that do best perfume the air.

—Francis Bacon

J U L Y

Everlastings

❧ Everlasting describes a specific group of annuals that can be air dried without losing form or color. Many of these flowers have dry, papery blooms even while they're growing.

❧ Everlastings include strawflower, statice, salvia, globe amaranth, nigella, helipterum, celosia, and lunaria.

❧ Grow everlastings from seed sown after the last expected frost in spring. The flowers will start blooming in midsummer.

❧ Pick flowers at midday, when the dew has dried and blooms are at their peak. For air drying, strip leaves from the stems, then gather the stems in small bunches.

❧ Hang the bunches upside down in a dark, dry place for two or three weeks.

1

2

3

4

5

6

7

8

9

10

11

12

13

14

15

Flowers leave some of their fragrance in the hand that bestows them.

—Chinese proverb

16

17

18

19

20

21

22

23

24

25

26

27

28

29

30

31

If the first of July be rainy weather,
It will rain, more or less, for four weeks together.

—English proverb

CHILDREN'S GARDENS

A CHILD'S FIRST GARDEN

To guarantee a successful first flower garden, start with a small plot (say, 3x6 feet), and locate it in a sunny spot within easy reach of a garden hose. Plant seeds in straight rows, using a string tied between two stakes. That way, pesky weed seedlings can be easily spotted and pulled. Buy bedding plants for eager young gardeners who can't wait for seeds to sprout.

Nothing is more completely the child of art than a garden.

—Sir Walter Scott

What to Plant?

Young gardeners just naturally like to touch and feel, pinch and pluck, and sniff and smell their way through a flower border. To satisfy all of their curious investigations, select species that offer not only bright blooms, but also sweet and spicy scents, and soft and rough leaf textures. Flowers such as zinnia, nasturtium, marigold, and cosmos grow quickly from seed and don't mind being picked again and again.

The peculiar characteristics of some flowers will also capture a child's interest. Sunflowers, for instance, are always a hit. Kids marvel at how poking a small seed into the earth can miraculously produce a flowering giant.

Create a cool, child-size hideaway by shaping a wire trellis tunnel from old fencing material. Plant gourds, pumpkins, and cucumbers next to the trellis, and by midsummer, it will be smothered by vines.

Growing Vegetables

Children love to be farmers and grow crops for family meals. Sowing seeds is half the fun. For little hands, choose crops with big seeds, such as peas, pumpkins, squash, cucumbers, and beans. To satisfy a child's eagerness for instant results, include a few crops that grow quickly, such as lettuce, radishes, and scallions.

Sweet peas, balloon vine, and scarlet runner beans cover the birch saplings that are woven together, tepee style, to form the arbor in the Fitch Garden at Old Sturbridge Village in Massachusetts. The arbor is part of a small ornamental garden described in the book The Young Florist; or Conversations on The Culture of Flowers, and on Natural History, *written in 1833 by Joseph Breck.*

31

AUGUST

Garden Paths

🍂 Keep garden paths at least three feet wide, which will allow two people to comfortably walk side by side.

🍂 A formal garden needs a formal path, such as pavers or brick. Stepping stones or tree rounds would suit a wildflower setting.

🍂 Curves add drama, especially if there's a special surprise around the bend, such as a gazebo or a pocket of snapdragons bursting with color.

🍂 Line the walkway with a jumble of colors and textures, such as ajuga, astilbe, hosta, impatiens, moss phlox, pachysandra, sweet alyssum, and vinca.

🍂 An underlayer of newspapers or a top coat of mulch can deter weeds.

1 _____

2 _____

3 _____

4 _____

5 _____

6 _____

7 _____

8 _____

9 _____

10 _____

11 _____

12 _____

13 _____

14 _____

15 _____

Earth laughs in flowers.

—*Ralph Waldo Emerson*

16 _____

17 _____

18 _____

19 _____

20 _____

21 _____

22 _____

23 _____

24 _____

25 _____

26 _____

27 _____

28 _____

29 _____

30 _____

31 _____

If the twenty-fourth of August be fair and clear,

Then hope for a prosperous Autumn that year.

—*English proverb*

Plans for the Season

_____

_____

_____

_____

_____

_____

_____

AUTUMN

Just before the death of flowers,
And before they are buried in the snow,
There comes a festival season
When Nature is all aglow.

—Anonymous

SEPTEMBER

Harvest Recipes

🌿 Zucchini Parmesan

Place 3 cups thinly sliced zucchini, 2 table-spoons butter, 1/2 teaspoon salt, and dash pepper in skillet. Cover and cook slowly for 5 minutes. Uncover and cook, turning slices, for 5 minutes more. Sprinkle with 2 table-spoons grated Parmesan cheese. Serves 4.

🌿 Chunky Applesauce

Pare, core, and slice 4 medium apples. Combine 1 cup water, 1/4 cup sugar, and dash mace; bring to a boil. Add apples; cover and simmer 8 minutes, or until tender.

1

2

3

4

5

6

7

8

9

10

11

12

13

14

15

16 _____

17 _____

18 _____

19 _____

20 _____

21 _____

22 _____

23 _____

24 _____

25 _____

26 _____

27 _____

28 _____

29 _____

30 _____

The garden continued its gorgeous appearance until the last of September, when there came a frost sufficiently heavy to destroy the tender annuals, which, when the sun arose, gave them a blackened and melancholy appearance; these Henry soon removed, and the garden was not entirely destitute of beauty, for many plants remained as bright as ever.

—Joseph Breck

*H*eaven is under our feet as well as over our heads.

—Henry David Thoreau

Planting Spring Bulbs

🌿 Plant bulbs as early in the fall as possible. This allows the bulbs to develop a root system before the ground freezes.

🌿 Improve soil drainage before you plant by adding organic matter such as peat moss, compost, leaf mold, or sand. Dense, wet soil can rot your bulbs.

🌿 Fertilize your bulbs when you plant them. Commercial products made specifically for bulbs are available.

🌿 Stretch chicken wire over the surface of your garden if chipmunks or squirrels try to dig up newly planted bulbs.

🌿 Next spring, after the plants bloom, let bulb foliage completely mature and turn yellow before you clip or mow the plants.

1

2

3

4

5

6

7

8

9

10

11

12

13

14

15

The tints of autumn—a mighty flower garden blossoming
under the spell of the enchanter, Frost.
—John Greenleaf Whittier

16

17

18

19

20

21

22

23

24

25

26

27

28

29

30

31

The sweet calm sunshine of October, now

Warms the low spot; upon its grassy mold

The purple oak-leaf falls; the birchen bough

Drops its bright spoil like arrow-heads of gold.

—W. C. Bryant

INDOOR BULB GARDENS

✳ To "force" bulbs to blossom ahead of schedule, place potted bulbs in a cold (35 to 50 degrees Fahrenheit), dark place, such as a refrigerator, unheated basement, or cold frame. Keep the soil moist.

✳ Allow 15 weeks from the time you pot bulbs until the time they bloom. Most bulbs require 12 weeks of cold for rooting, and another three weeks at room temperature to flower.

✳ Tulips need a 15-week rooting period; narcissus need only three weeks.

✳ Move pots to a cool room in your house, away from direct sunlight, when stems are an inch or two high and roots are growing through the drainage holes.

✳ When shoots are about 4 inches tall, set pots in a warm, bright area to stimulate blooming. Continue to keep the soil moist.

Once the gardening season is over, look for dried grasses, flowers, weeds, and berries to create indoor decorations. You can shape them into wreaths, tabletop Christmas trees, swags, or bouquets.

Clay pots are excellent for houseplants because they let the plants breathe. However, they also absorb moisture, drawing water out of the soil and robbing the plant. To avoid this, completely immerse new pots in a pail of water. Let them remain there until all hissing stops. (The hissing will be barely audible, but you will hear it if you lean close to the water.)

In the depths of winter, I finally learned that within me there lay an invincible summer.

—*Albert Camus*

Orange and Pomegranate Wreath

Enjoy nature's bounty with this easy-to-make decoration.

Materials: Dried oranges and pomegranates; bay leaves; dried moss; plastic foam wreath of desired size; hot-glue gun; wire for hanging.

Instructions: Cover wreath form with moss; glue in place. Glue oranges and pomegranates in place, positioning as desired. Glue bay leaves between fruits to fill in gaps. Attach wire to back for hanging.

NOVEMBER

Putting Perennials to Bed

꙳ Give perennials winter protection after the first killing frost. First, cut and remove dead stalks, trimming stems to within 4 inches of the ground.

꙳ When the beds have been cleared of all dead foliage and weeds, apply a winter mulch of straw or peat moss. This can be held down by sections of chicken wire or branches.

꙳ Some plants, such as the poppy and madonna lily, put up a small tuft of growth in the fall that needs extra protection. A flowerpot covering it will keep mulch from flattening the leaves.

꙳ If fall rains have been light, deeply water the perennials.

1 _____

2 _____

3 _____

4 _____

5 _____

6 _____

7 _____

8 _____

9 _____

10 _____

11 _____

12 _____

13 _____

14 _____

15 _____

The North wind doth blow, And we shall have snow,
And what will the robin do then, poor thing?

—Anonymous, Nursery Rhyme

16 _____

17 _____

18 _____

19 _____

20 _____

21 _____

22 _____

23 _____

24 _____

25 _____

26 _____

27 _____

28 _____

29 _____

30 _____

No warmth, no cheerfulness, no healthful ease—
No comfortable feel in any member—
No shade, no shine, no butterflies, no bees,
No fruits, no flowers, no leaves, no birds,
No-vember!

—Thomas Hood

Natural Christmas Wreath

Materials: Wire box frame in desired size; Spanish moss; monofilament; various dried flowers, weeds, and grasses as available and as desired; grapevine (if desired); craft glue or hot-glue gun; floral wire and tape; floral picks.

Instructions: *Note:* Wire box frame is a round, domed wreath base made of four parallel wires. Wrap frame with Spanish moss; secure with monofilament. If desired, wrap grapevine around frame. Glue dried materials in place, arranging and spacing as desired. If needed, dried materials can be attached to floral picks with wire and tape.

1
2
3
4
5
6
7
8
9
10
11
12
13
14
15

Deep snow in the Winter; tall grain in the Summer.
—*Estonian proverb*

16

17

18

19

20

21

22

23

24

25

26

27

28

29

30

31

At Christmas time we deck the hall
With holly branches brave and tall,
With sturdy pine and hemlock bright
And in the Yule log's dancing light
We tell old tales of field and fight
At Christmas time.

—*English traditional*

*T*he trumpet of a prophecy!
O Wind,
If Winter comes,
can Spring be far behind?
—*P.B. Shelley*